I want to be healthier.

D0531338

Life Canvas:

Diet Doodle Diary

In which I record my

Small but SIGNIFICANT *slimming* TRIUMPHS

Illustrated by Julie Sweeney

First published by Exclusive Editions Publishing Ltd in 2013
LIFE CANVAS is an imprint of Exclusive Editions Publishing Ltd

Copyright © 2012 Waverley Books

LIFE CANVAS and the accompanying logo are trademarks of Exclusive Editions Publishing Ltd

Illustrations by Julie Mackey
Typeset by Waverley Books in Prophecy Script (© Tension Type) and Secret Service Typewriter (© Red Rooster) fonts

Diet Doodle Diary contains real-life tips from genuinely successful slimmers: Sandy Fleming, Gill Brown, Susan MacMillan, Sarah Robertson, Jillian Stewart and Marie Jo McCrossan

All rights reserved. No part of this publication may be reproduced, stored in a retrieval system or transmitted, in any form or by any means, electronic, mechanical, photocopying, recording or otherwise, without the prior permission of the copyright holder.

ISBN 978-1-78186-826-3
GTIN 5060292801063

Printed in China

Consult your doctor before following any new diet or fitness plans.

plan your MEALS!

The *Diet Doodle Diary* is more than a log book for your food and exercise.

Write in it, read it, doodle, be inspired and laugh. Every page has something to amuse, advise or make you think.

There are weight-loss secrets from real slimmers who've been there and learned the hard way. Every page has a tip to make losing weight easier.

With humorous illustrations by artist Julie Mackey, this book is the most fun you'll ever have keeping a weight-loss log!

Log your exercise progress

Record Your Measurements

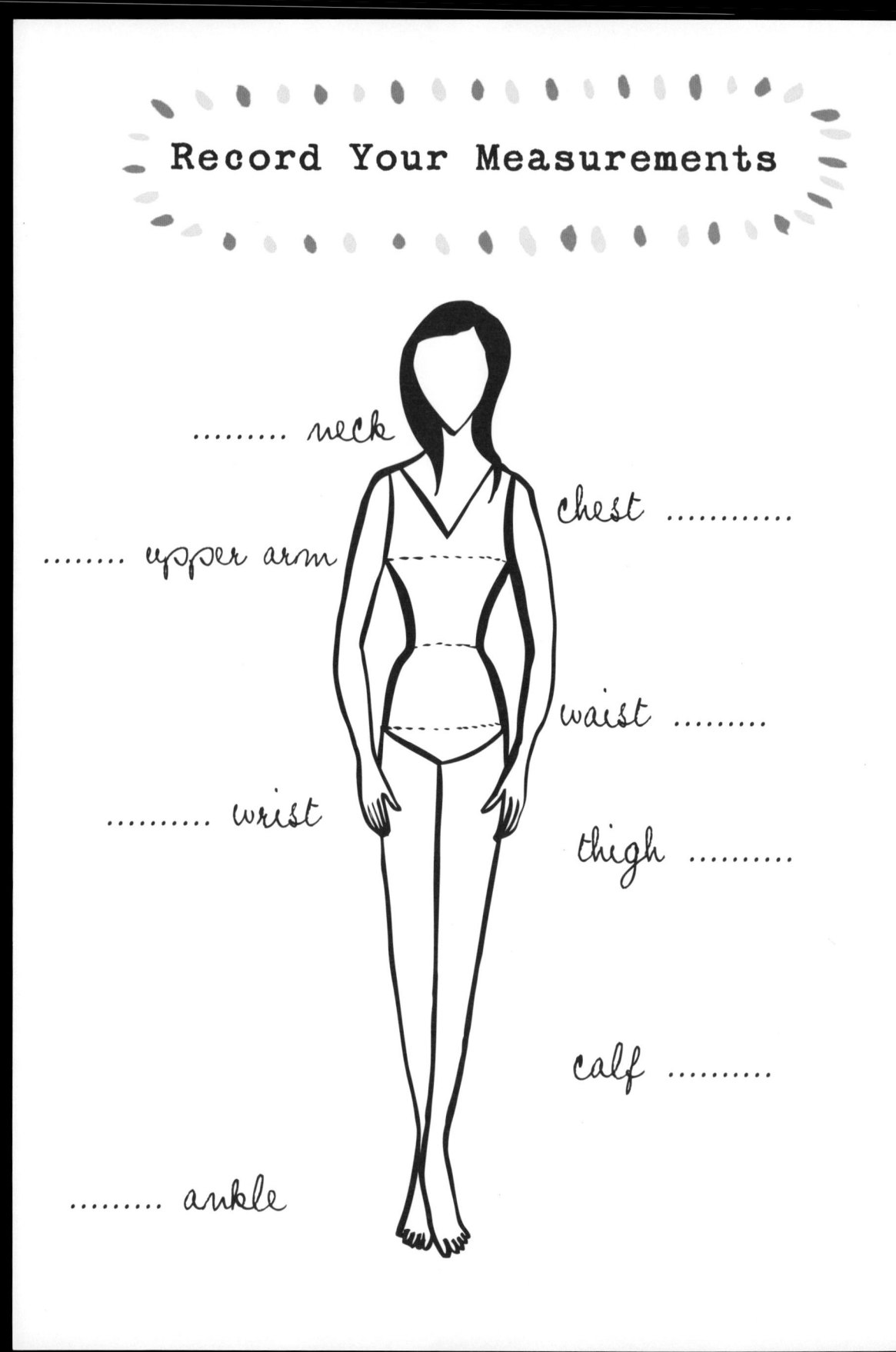

.... neck

chest ....

.... upper arm

waist ....

.... wrist

thigh ....

calf ....

.... ankle

Today's Date:

THE weigh-IN

Starting weight:

Resting heart rate:

TIP: How to find your resting heart rate.

On waking, take your pulse using three fingers. Find the pulse in your wrist or your neck — whichever is easier. Count how many heartbeats you can feel in six seconds. Multiply by ten to find how many beats per minute. Write this number in the box above. Every so often throughout the book you'll have space to record this to see how your fitness is improving.

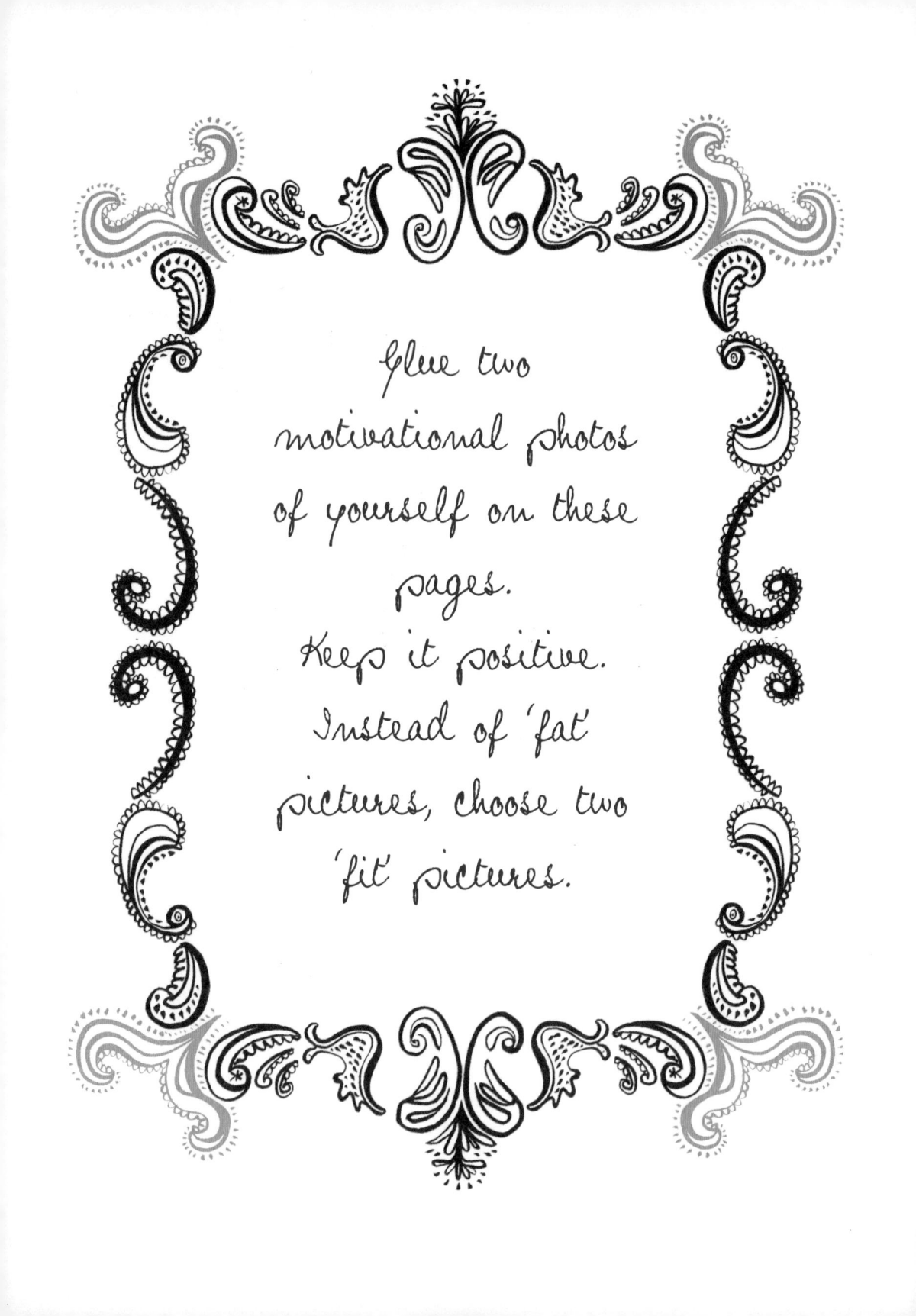

Glue two
motivational photos
of yourself on these
pages.
Keep it positive.
Instead of 'fat'
pictures, choose two
'fit' pictures.

Think of a time when you were slimmer or when you were feeling happy and active, even as a child. If you've been there before, you can get there again.

'Diet starts on Monday?'

M	M	M	M	M	M	M
	1	2				
3	4	5	6	7	8	9
10	11	12	13	14	15	16
17	18	19	20	21	22	23
24	25	26	27	28	29	30

... your healthy eating plan can start any day,
don't wait for Monday!

Start by getting rid of all the
rubbish in your cupboards.

Don't think of it as wasted. It was already rubbish when you bought it.

Start keeping a food diary today.

You'll find it helpful to write down everything that you eat.

FOOD DIARY

- 30g Cornflakes
- Skimmed Milk
- Apple
- Coffee
- Yoghurt

- Egg Sandwich
- Orange
- Fruit Salad
- Sugar Free Hot Chocolate

three packets of smoky bacon crisps and a chocolate bar

Be honest!

Details matter — don't miss the little 'extras'.

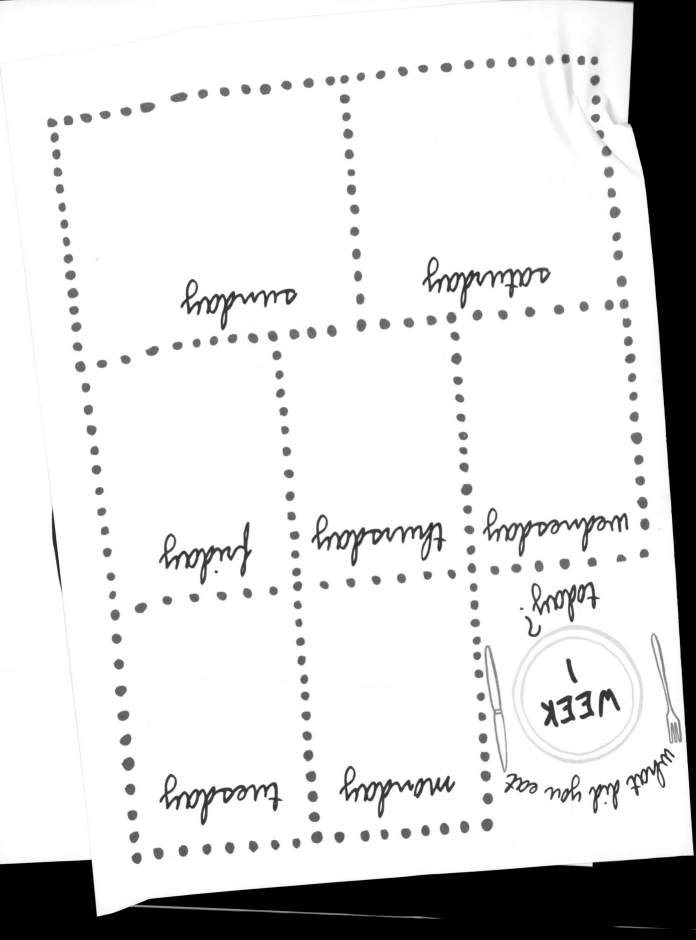

what did you eat today?

WEEK 1

sunday

saturday

friday

thursday

wednesday

tuesday

monday

WHAT ARE **YOUR** FITNESS goals?

(circle) any of the ones you fancy

WEEK 2

Food
Diary

sunday

saturday

friday

thursday

wednesday

tuesday

monday

THE weigh-IN

WEIGHT : _____
WAIST : _____
HEART RATE : _____

sunday

saturday

friday

thursday

wednesday

tuesday

monday

EXERCISE LOG
WEEK 2

Draw the contents of
your fridge, as it looks
now — be honest !

Draw the contents of your fridge, as it is going to look once you've been shopping for healthy food.

'By failing to prepare, you are preparing to fail.'
-Benjamin Franklin

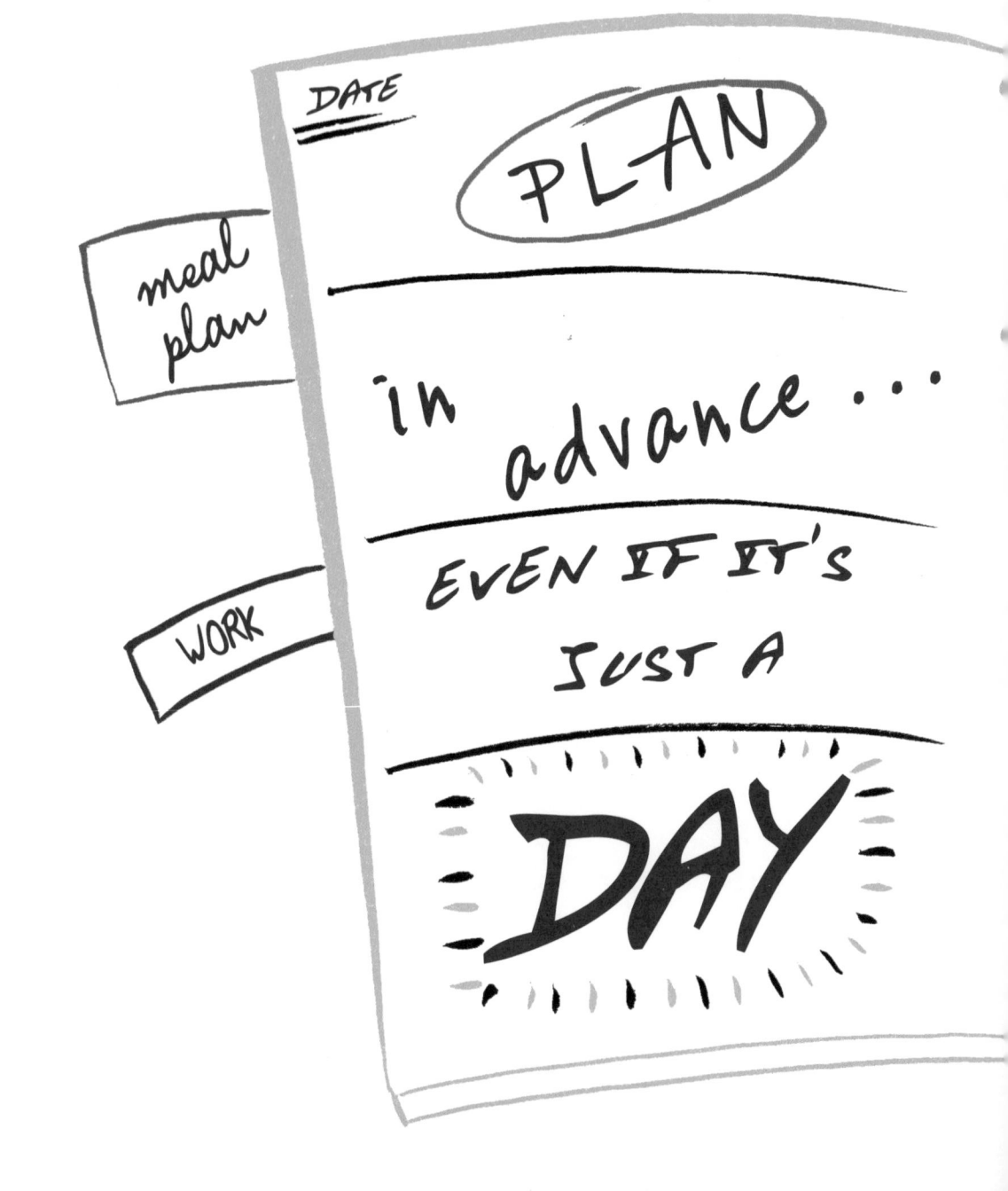

If you plan ahead

You will be LESS

likely to...

SWAY from IT!

SHOPPING LIST

exercise plan

Laundry

SOCIAL LIFE!

WEEK 3

FOOD DIARY

monday

tuesday

wednesday

thursday

friday

saturday

sunday

EXERCISE LOG
WEEK 3

monday

tuesday

wednesday

thursday

friday

saturday

sunday

THE Weigh-IN

WEIGHT : _____

WAIST : _____

HEART RATE : _____

REMEMBER: Record your rest and stretch days too.

How do you feel ?

Choose descriptive words and write them
in the thought bubbles. We'll do this again later.

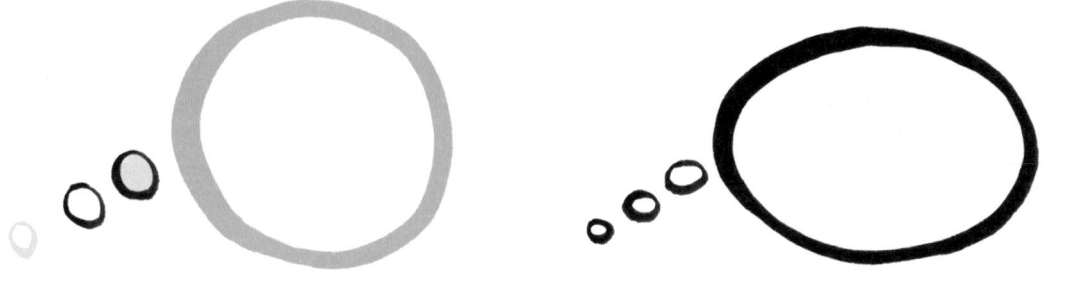

grumpy
motivated
happy hungry
excited
sad hopeful

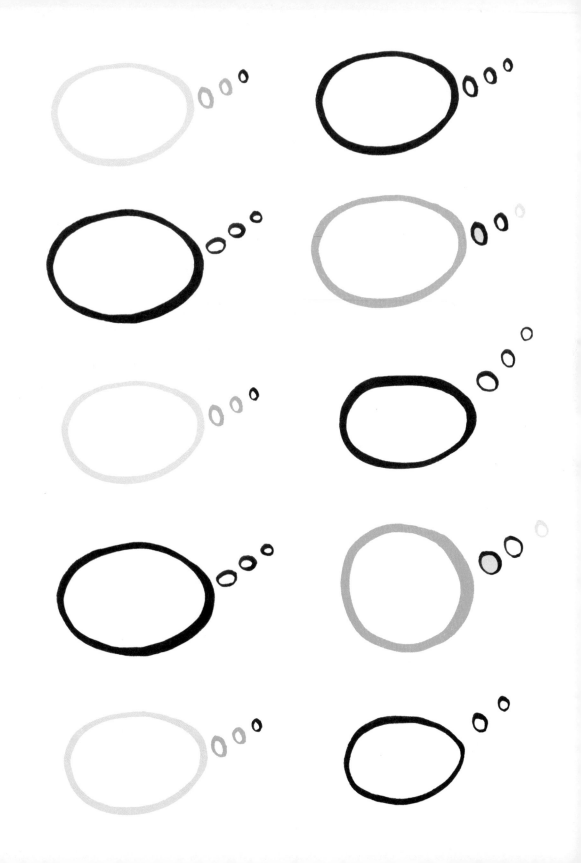

Fitting into skinny jeans is my next goal!'

Goals don't have to be about the number on the scales.

My Goals

Write down what your long-term goals are (we'll revisit them later and see how many you've achieved).

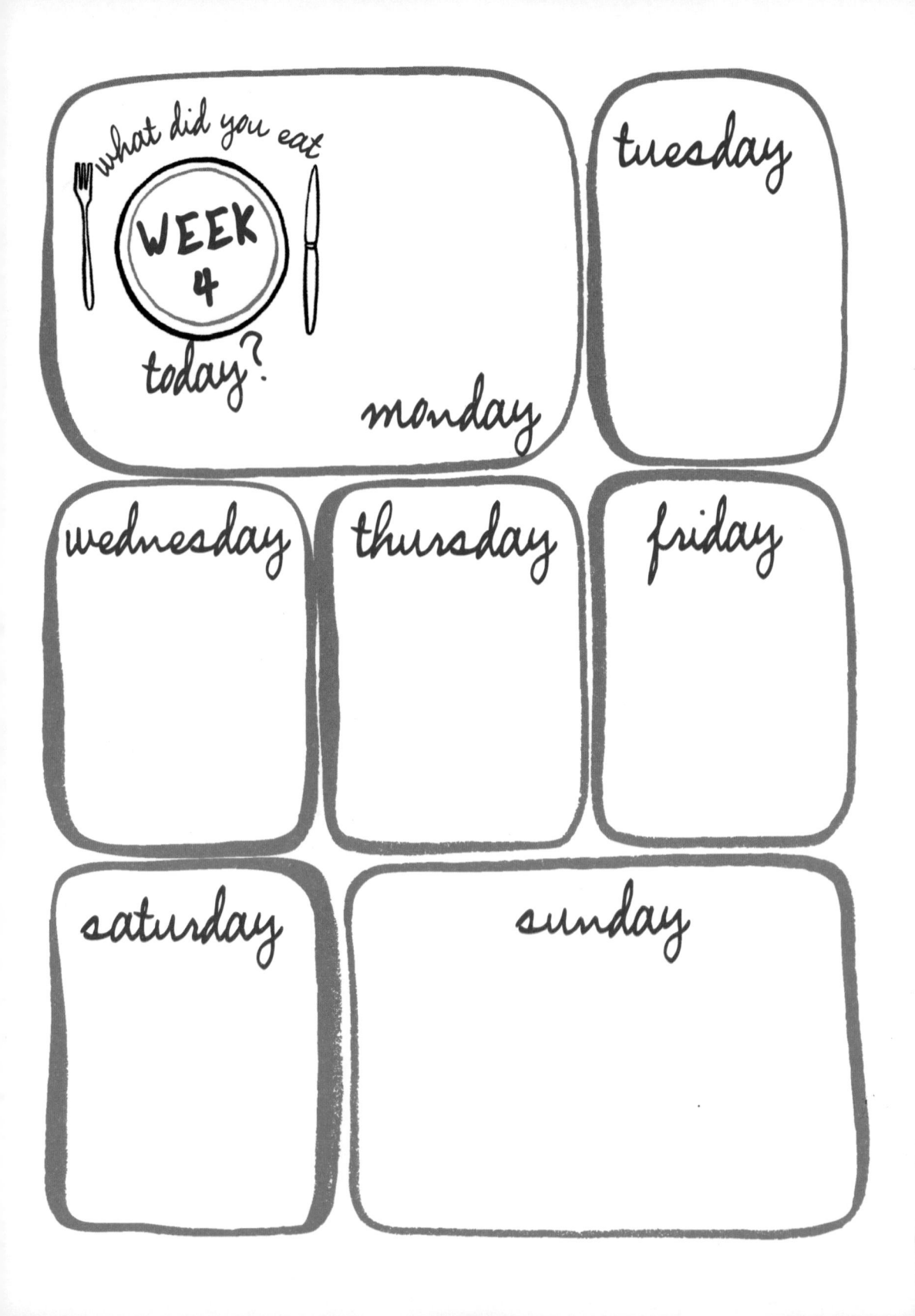

WEEK 4

Log your exercise progress

monday

tuesday

wednesday

thursday

friday

saturday

sunday

THE weigh-IN

WEIGHT :

WAIST :

HEART RATE :

THOSE SKINNY JEANS

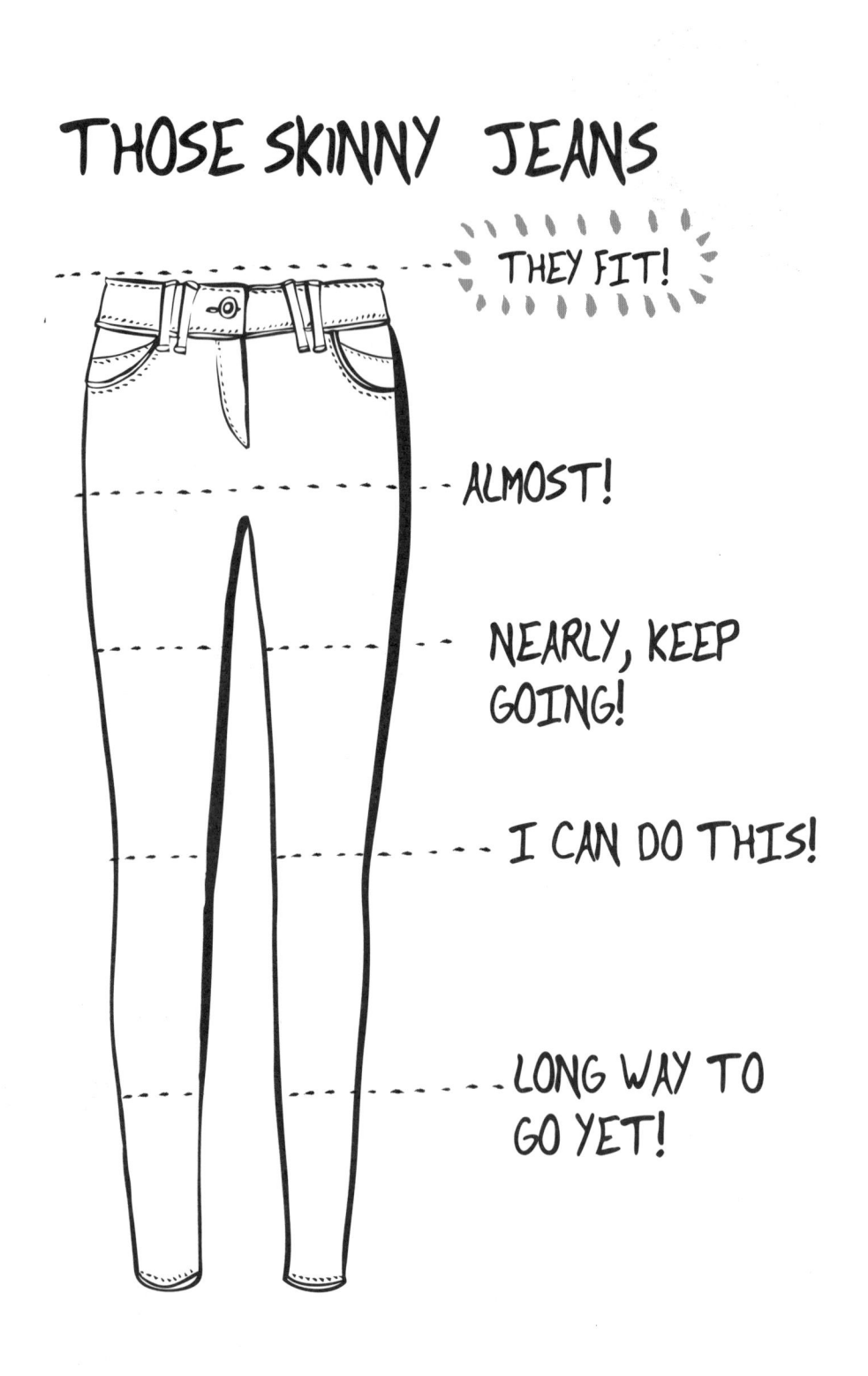

THEY FIT!

ALMOST!

NEARLY, KEEP GOING!

I CAN DO THIS!

LONG WAY TO GO YET!

Skinny Jeans, or the perfect little dress — too tight and still with the tags on. We've all got something like that in our wardrobes! Well, you said you'd 'slim into it', so use it as a goal. On the opposite page, shade how far you've come in your quest to fit that impulse purchase.

Then post your picture here when it fits!

monday

tuesday

wednesday

thursday

friday

saturday

sunday

WEEK
5

FOOD DIARY

monday

tuesday

EXERCISE LOG
WEEK 5

wednesday

thursday

friday

saturday

sunday

THE
Weigh-
IN

WEIGHT : _____
WAIST : _____
HEART
RATE : _____

Be kind to yourself. Don't say things to yourself that you would never dream of saying to anyone else.

Draw or

write ten things

you like about

yourself

in the hearts.

What did you eat today?

WEEK 6

monday

tuesday

wednesday

thursday

friday

saturday

sunday

Do **YOUR** Best

Don't compare yourself to others

Don't aim for perfection

Be the best that **YOU** can be

Track Your Progress ...

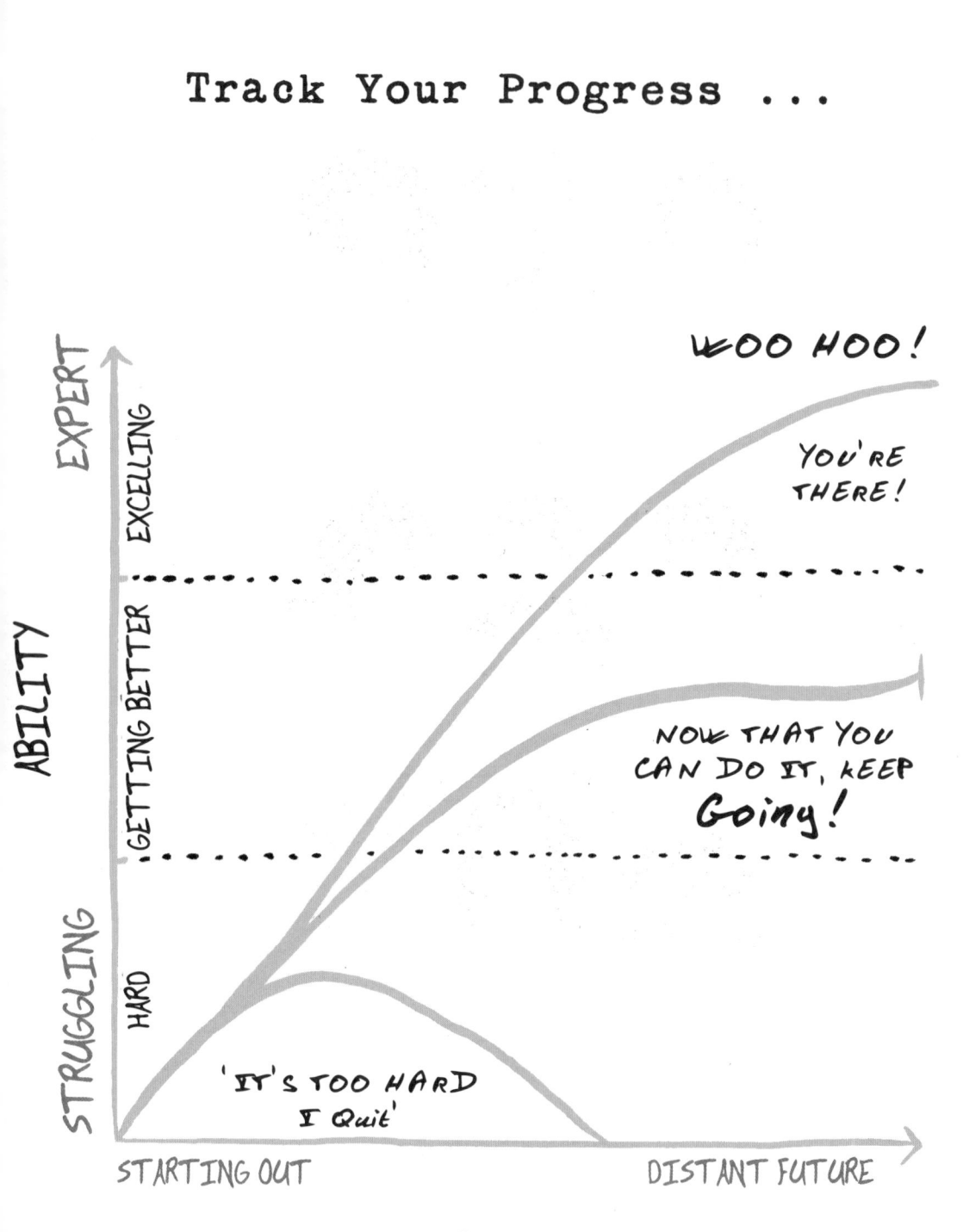

Let's see the line on the
graph go up and up as your
weight comes down and down.

WEIGHT LOSS IN POUNDS

105
100
95
90
85
80
75
70
65
60
55
50
45
40
35
30
25
20
15
10
5

2 4 6 8 10 12 14 16 18 20 22 24 24 26 28 30
WEEKS

THE weigh-IN

WEIGHT :
WAIST :
HEART RATE :

sunday

saturday

friday

thursday

wednesday

tuesday

monday

Log your exercise progress

Week 6

Don't buy multipacks of your favourite snacks as snacks even if it is a 'bargain'.

DANGER!

100% empty calories

FATTY PUFFS

26 PACK

WARNING: Could easily be eaten at once.

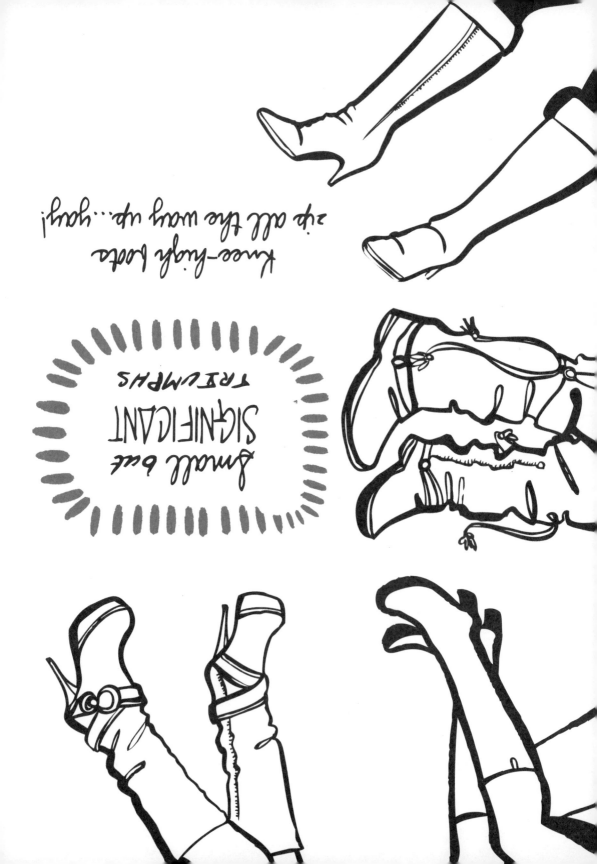

Knee-high boots
zip all the way up...yay!

Small but
SIGNIFICANT
TRIUMPHS

"Whatever I wear today, the boots are going on!"

sunday

saturday

friday   thursday   wednesday

WEEK 4
EXERCISE LOG

tuesday   monday

selection of fruit

What I ate today

skimmed milk

30g cereal and

tea...

...water

...or coffee

Leave home feeling full up.

Have a drink, fruit and cereal for breakfast.

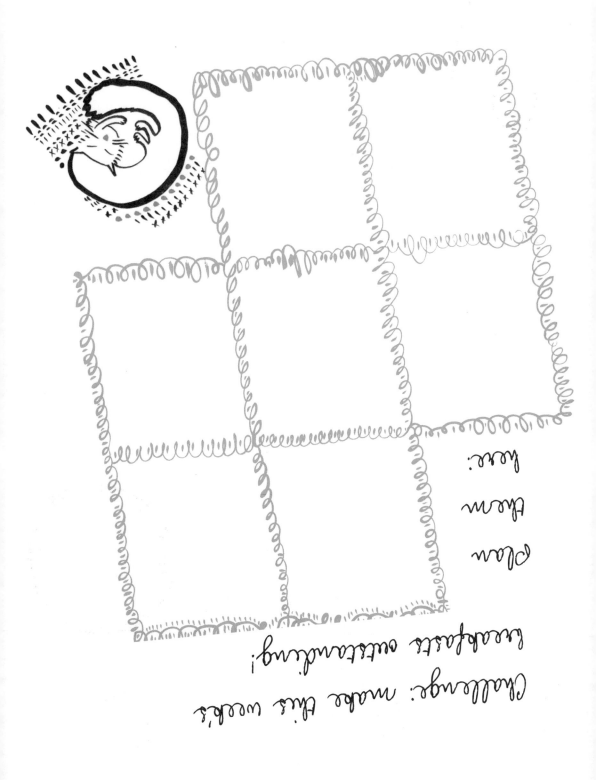

Challenge: make this week's breakfasts outstanding!

Plan them here:

WEIGHT :

WAIST :

HEART RATE :

THE weigh-IN

sunday

saturday

friday

thursday

wednesday

WEEK 7

What did
you eat
today?

tuesday

monday

Don't eat the same thing every day ...
... even if at first you love it. You'll get very bored.

List your favourite ingredients here ...

Now go and look up some new recipes
using them. Regularly write new recipes
in the spaces provided in this book.

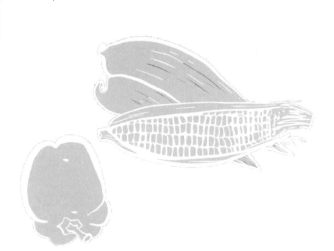

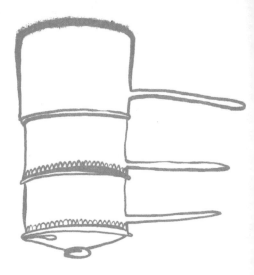

my new recipes

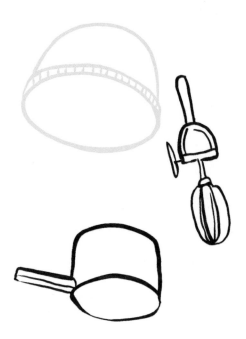

If what you are doing is not WORKING – GUESS WHAT? Change what you are DOING!

How do you feel about your progress so far? What small things could you change that might improve your weight loss?

EXERCISE LOG
WEEK 8

sunday

saturday

friday

thursday

wednesday

tuesday

monday

Write an
alternative holiday
checklist.

holiday checklist

This checklist isn't going to include a passport and sunscreen but might include fitting comfortably into an airline seat and not giving up your healthy eating or your jogging plan because you are on holiday.

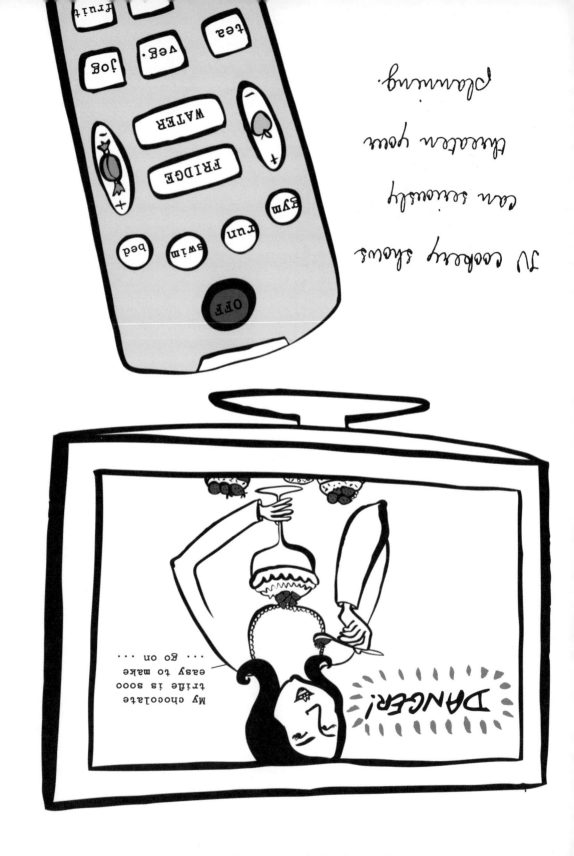

WEEK 8

THE weigh-IN

WEIGHT :
WAIST :
HEART RATE :

sunday

saturday

friday

thursday

wednesday

tuesday

monday

WHAT DID YOU EAT TODAY?

I'm seeing smaller
pants on my washing line ...

This week my

Small but
SIGNIFICANT
TRIUMPH

is ...

sunday

saturday

friday

thursday

wednesday

tuesday

monday

What did
you eat
today?

WEEK 9

EXERCISE LOG

WEEK 9

monday

tuesday

wednesday

thursday

friday

saturday

sunday

THE weigh-IN

WEIGHT : _____

WAIST : _____

HEART
RATE : _____

Remember to stretch! And drink water!

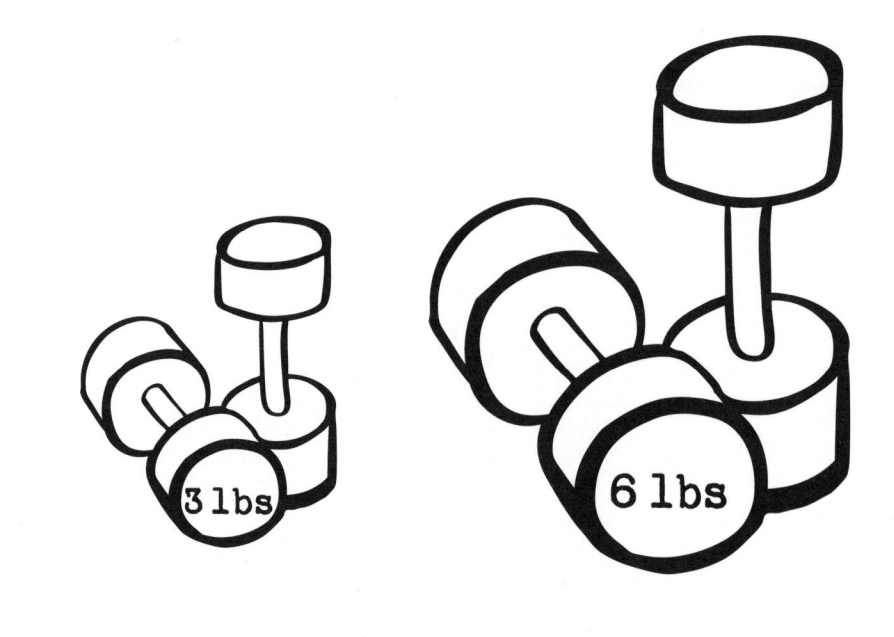

Weights: Day 1   Weights: Day 24

Track your progress.
What seems impossible at the
beginning will get easier
every time you do it.

Does your wardrobe need a clear-out?

This week's challenge: Clear-out your too-big clothes, clear out your too-small clothes, clear out your unflattering tents and your worn-out baggy stuff. Coordinate and organize what's left to make the most of your figure.

Write or draw here what you need to buy to
complete your current wardrobe:

WEEK 10

What did you eat today?

monday

tuesday

wednesday

thursday

friday

saturday

sunday

THE weigh-IN

WEIGHT :
WAIST :
HEART
RATE :

sunday

saturday

friday

thursday

wednesday

tuesday

monday

Exercise is time to yourself – time to think.

Exercise is more than 'keeping fit'.

Write down the things you get from exercise other than weight loss.

Lunch isn't for wimps.

But don't have the same
thing every day. Write some
sparkling lunch ideas here
— bagels, wraps, flatbread,
savoury rice ...

Log your exercise progress

week 11

sunday

saturday

friday

thursday

wednesday

tuesday

monday

THE weigh-IN

WEIGHT :
WAIST :
HEART RATE :

sunday

saturday

friday

thursday

wednesday

tuesday

monday

WEEK 11

What did you eat today?

Are you noticing patterns in your food choices?

Don't play the lunchtime lottery at the sandwich bar ... Pack your own lunch.

Challenge!

DON'T MAKE WEIGHT LOSS YOUR ONLY GOAL.
CHALLENGE YOURSELF:

Get more sleep

Be more organized,
pre-cook the week's meals

Learn new Recipes

Take a new class

Get a fitness goal

Drink more water

Meet more people

Look more groomed

Make a packed lunch

Colour the boxes when they become a regular thing.

Write seven challenges here:

What could you challenge yourself to do?

You don't have to be a SAINT, just be honest with yourself. You can't eat cakes or sweets EVERY DAY and lose weight.

THE weigh-IN

WEIGHT :
WAIST :
HEART RATE :

sunday

saturday

friday

thursday

wednesday

monday

tuesday

WEEK 12

Log your exercise progress

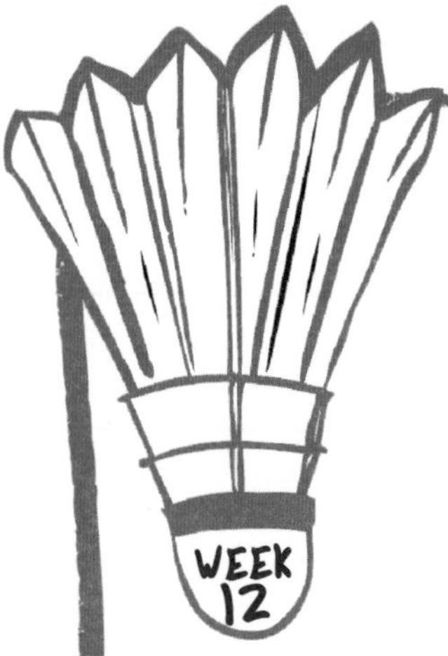

Don't feed your emotions . . .

What did you eat today?

WEEK 12

monday

tuesday

wednesday   thursday   friday

saturday   sunday

... deal with problems in other ways, not with food.

'I can wrap the bath towel all the way round me now ... it may seem daft to anyone else but this has made me happy and proud.'

This week my

Small but SIGNIFICANT TRIUMPH

is ...

FAST or Slow?

EAT SLOWER.

Set a timer and make sure you take at least 20 minutes to eat every meal.

PUT THE fork Down.

TICK TOCK

chew everything properly.

really TASTE your food and enjoy it!

monday

tuesday

wednesday

thursday

friday

plan
your
DINNERS!

saturday

sunday

WEEK 13

Things are more fun when you do them with someone else – get a buddy to join you for exercise.

monday

tuesday

EXERCISE LOG

WEEK 13

wednesday

thursday

friday

saturday

sunday

THE weigh-IN

WEIGHT :

WAIST :

HEART RATE :

You
don't need to go to
the GYM
to get your exercise.
Throw yourself into
everything you do ...
WITH GUSTO!

What activities could you add a
little more action to?
Write them here:

sunday

saturday

friday

thursday

wednesday

tuesday

monday

what did you eat today?

WEEK 14

EXERCISE LOG

WEEK 14

monday

tuesday

wednesday

thursday

friday

saturday

sunday

THE weigh-IN

WEIGHT :

WAIST :

HEART RATE :

my NEW recipes

WEEK 15

what did you eat today?

sunday

saturday

friday

thursday

wednesday

tuesday

monday

Food before:
spaghetti and wine
and garlic bread

Food after: still
looks good!

Writing down your
goals makes it
more likely that
you'll strive to
achieve them...

'Like this?'

I
want to be
healthier

... erm ...

... you don't
have to wear
the T-shirt.

Just write them down and keep them in a
place where you will see them every day.

Log your fitness progress

THE Weigh-IN

WEIGHT: _____

WAIST: _____

HEART RATE: _____

sunday

saturday

friday

thursday

wednesday

tuesday

monday

This
is a treat box.
Inside it you can stash
some lovely non-food treats
for days when you need a
little boost. A face mask, a
funny DVD, bath oil, nail
varnish ...

On the next page,
write or draw what you
could put in your own
treat box.
Then make one!

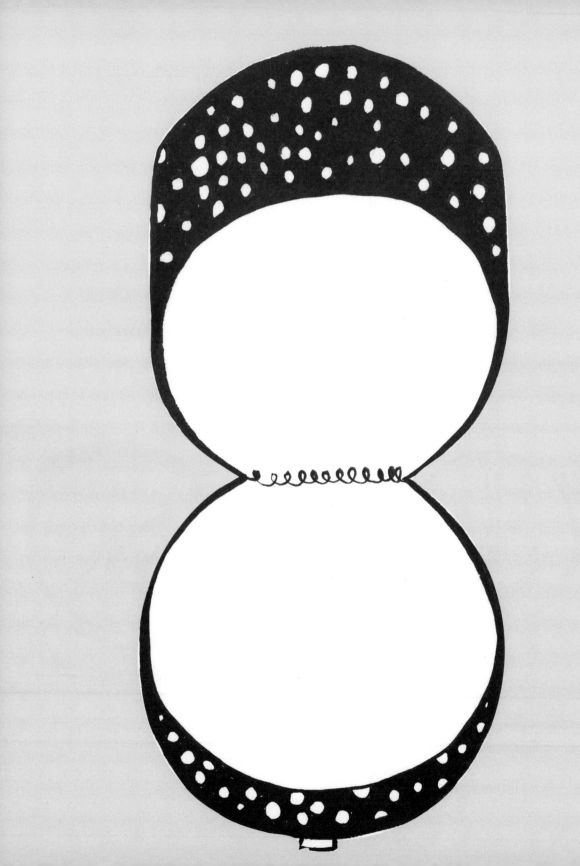

Get on your bike

How many times have you used the car this week?
Taken the bus? The train?

Get around under your own steam as much as you can
this week. Walk, cycle (wear a helmet, even if it
ruins your hair), even run if you can.

If you can't do it the whole way, then just do
it some of the way. Allow yourself the time to
increase your activity.

WEEK 16

What did you eat today?

monday

tuesday

wednesday

thursday

friday

saturday

sunday

Have you ever been
on a fad diet?
Haven't we all? Do they work?
Well if they did would
you be reading this?
Don't starve or deprive
yourself, it never works
in the long run...

WEEK 16

Log your fitness progress

THE weigh-IN

WEIGHT : _____
WAIST : _____
HEART
RATE : _____

sunday

saturday

friday

thursday

wednesday

tuesday

monday

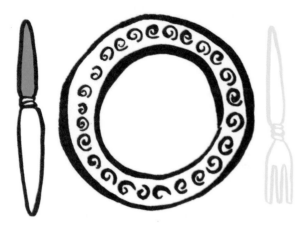

my new recipes

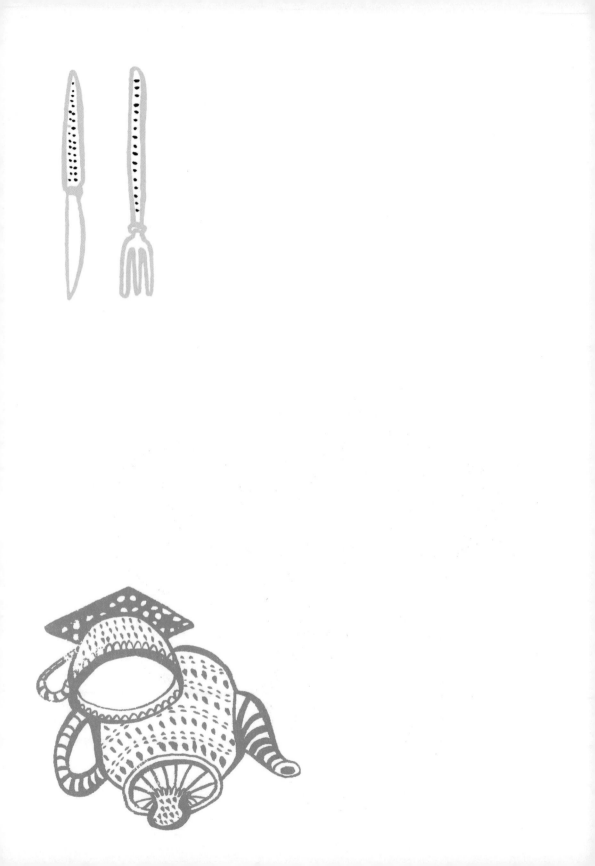

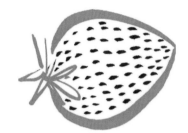

Shade a segment of
one of these fruits
– one fruit for each
day this week – when
you've eaten one of your
five-a-day fruits or
vegetables.

COLOUR IN
YOUR 5 A DAY

WEEK 17

What did you eat today?

sunday

saturday

friday

thursday

wednesday

tuesday

monday

Make this a week where you
don't sit still!
Shade a segment of the
bicycle every time you do
some kind of activity for
a few minutes at a time,
even a little walk, or some
housework, or taking the stairs
instead of the lift.
Fill in the whole bike!
Don't forget to stretch and to
rest.

 light

 medium

strenuous

Challenge: how many times can you
get active this week?

sunday

saturday

THE weigh-IN

WEIGHT :
WAIST :
HEART
RATE :

friday

thursday

wednesday

tuesday

monday

EXERCISE LOG

WEEK 17

What did you eat today?

sunday

saturday

friday

thursday

wednesday

tuesday

monday

THE weigh-IN

WEIGHT :
WAIST :
HEART RATE :

sunday

saturday

friday

thursday

wednesday

tuesday

monday

WEEK 18

Exercise Log

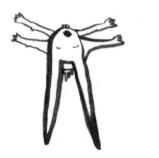 

will get you there!

steady

and

slow

This is not a RACE

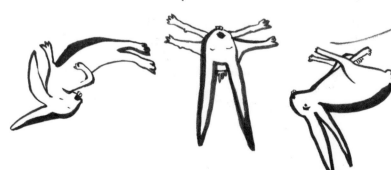

Don't become a diet bore ...

I do wish they would put calorie counts on menus. Did you know there's hidden butter and sugar in soup, and I never touch prawn crackers, and as for mayonnaise, well I'd ban it ...

badly suppressed yawn

Z Z z z

sunday

saturday

friday

thursday

wednesday

tuesday

monday

WEEK 19

what did you eat today?

THE weigh-IN
WEIGHT :
WAIST :
HEART RATE :

sunday

saturday

friday

thursday

wednesday

tuesday

monday

WEEK 19

Log your fitness progress

Wear clothes
that fit.
Only triangular-
shaped people
should wear tents.

'NOTHING IS IMPOSSIBLE,

THE WORD ITSELF SAYS

"I'm possible"!'

—AUDREY HEPBURN

THE weigh-IN

WEIGHT :
WAIST :
HEART RATE :

sunday

saturday

friday

thursday

wednesday

monday

tuesday

what did you eat today?

WEEK
20

New

Something

Try

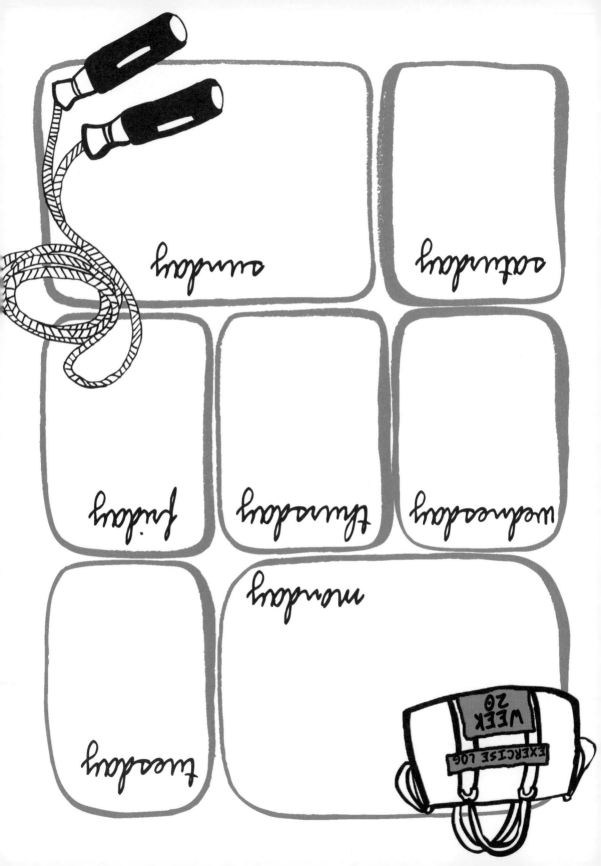

an apple a day . . .

Pink Lady

Cox

Granny Smith

Stick the stickers from your five-a-day fruits on this page.

sunday

saturday

friday

thursday

wednesday

monday

tuesday

food diary
WEEK 21

sunday

THE weigh-IN

WEIGHT :

WAIST :

HEART RATE :

saturday

friday

thursday

wednesday

tuesday

monday

EXERCISE LOG

WEEK 21

SKIPPING MEALS WILL
LEAVE YOU HUNGRY
AND FEELING LIKE A
GRIZZLY BEAR!

Visualise yourself getting slimmer.

Draw yourself getting slimmer.

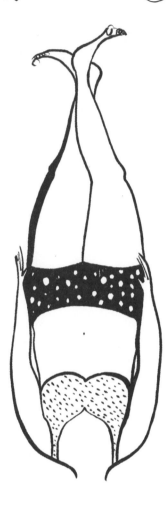

THE weigh-IN

WEIGHT :
WAIST :
HEART RATE :

sunday

saturday

friday

thursday

wednesday

tuesday

monday

WEEK 22

What did you eat today?

sunday

saturday

friday

thursday

wednesday

tuesday

monday

WEEK 22

EXERCISE LOG

No more excuses...

Write your negative
thoughts on this page.
Turn the page and decide
that is the end of them.

'I can't eat that!'

I can't go into that shop

'The gym scares me'

'I don't like vegetables'

what did you eat

WEEK
23

today?

sunday

saturday

friday

thursday

wednesday

tuesday

monday

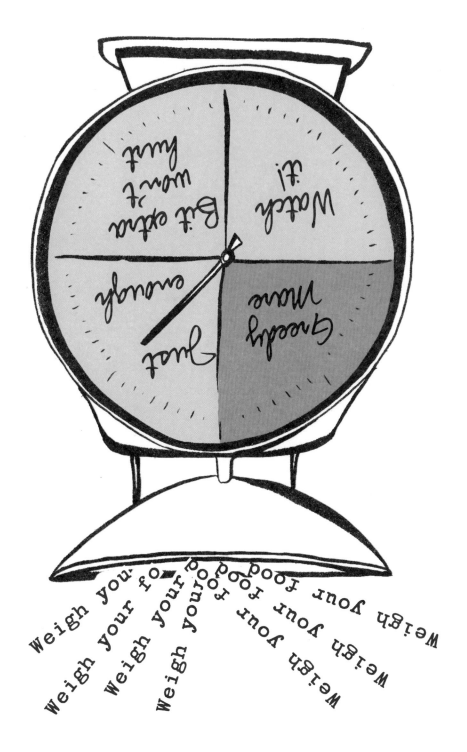

THE weigh-IN

WEIGHT : _____
WAIST : _____
HEART : _____
RATE

saturday

sunday

wednesday

thursday

friday

monday

tuesday

WEEK 23
EXERCISE LOG

Small but SIGNIFICANT TRIUMPH

There's extra room
next to me on the bus for my friends!

Dancing like an idiot is good exercise.
Don't avoid nights out because you are 'on
a diet'. Plan! And make good choices.

monday

tuesday

wednesday

thursday

friday

saturday

sunday

What did you eat today?

WEEK 24

LAST PLACE

So you're not the best cook in the world or the fittest person in your Zumba class ... it doesn't matter.

You don't need to be the best to make life better.

'Never discourage anyone who continually makes PROGRESS, no matter how slow.'
– PLATO

monday

EXERCISE LOG
WEEK 24

tuesday

wednesday

thursday

friday

saturday

sunday

THE weigh-IN

WEIGHT : _____

WAIST : _____

HEART
RATE : _____

What did you eat today?

sunday

saturday

friday

thursday

wednesday

tuesday

monday

Sunday

Saturday

Friday

Thursday

Wednesday

Tuesday

Monday

log your fitness progress

THE Weigh IN

WEIGHT: _____
WAIST: _____
HEART RATE: _____

'Our wedding rings fit again.'

What's your

small but
SIGNIFICANT
TRIUMPH

this week?

THE weigh-IN

WEIGHT :
WAIST :
HEART RATE :

sunday

saturday

friday

thursday

wednesday

tuesday

monday

WEEK 26

What did
you eat
today?

Get enough sleep!
Sleep helps you cope with most
things, including healthy eating.

z
z
z
Z

sunday

saturday

friday

thursday

wednesday

tuesday

monday

EXERCISE LOG
WEEK 26

plan your
DINNERS!

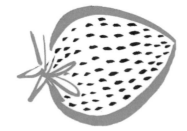

My New Recipes

Jannah.

are a good Size
for Rice
Puddings.

dishes.

SMALLER

FROM

EAT

It's not over ... WELL DONE!

You are changing your lifestyle and eating for the better. You are not on a diet that has a beginning and an end. This is a positive change for life!

Start Don't look at getting to target as an end point. **Start**

What did you eat today?

sunday

saturday

friday

thursday

wednesday

tuesday

monday

sunday

saturday

friday

thursday

wednesday

tuesday

monday

THE Weigh IN

WEIGHT :
WAIST :
HEART RATE :

EXERCISE LOG
WEEK 27

A hungry tummy is not a good chopping companion.

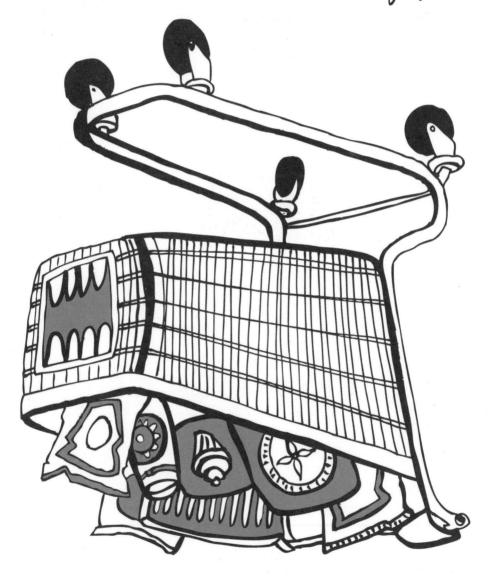

Reward yourself

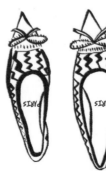

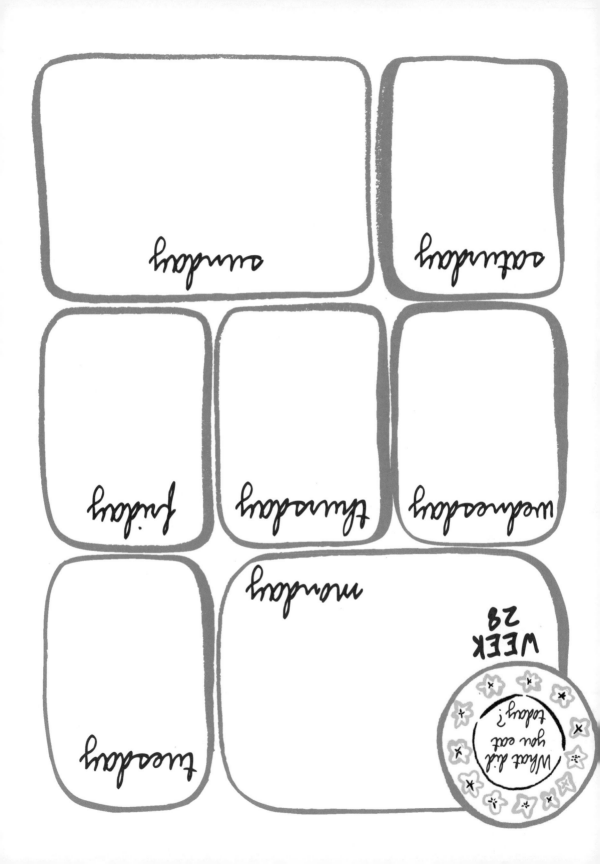

sunday

saturday

friday

thursday

wednesday

monday

WEEK
28

What did
you eat
today?

tuesday

How do you feel now?

Choose descriptive words and write them
in the thought bubbles.

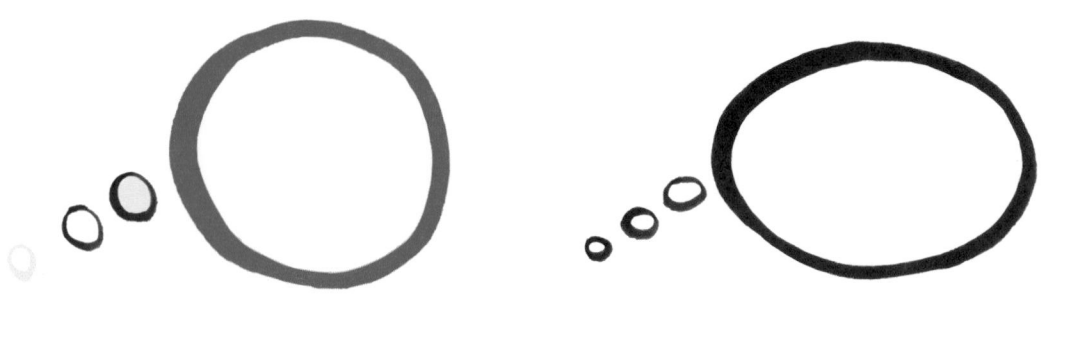

energized

healthy   happy

fearful   fit

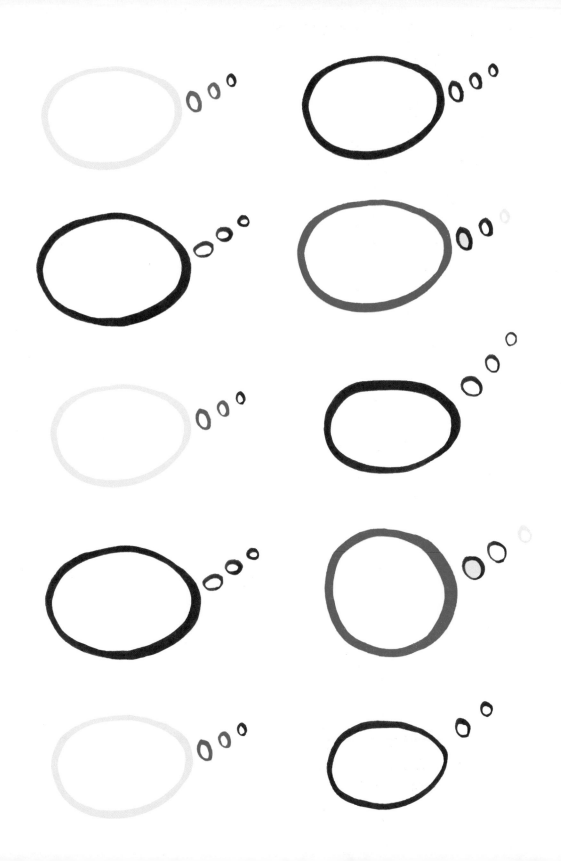

How far are you now from
your target weight?
Draw it on the scale.

It doesn't matter how far
you've come as long as
you are still
making PROGRESS.

Record your

measurements now:

Neck

. . . .

Chest

. . . .

Waist

. . . .

Upper arm

. . . .

Wrist

. . . .

Thigh

. . . .

Calf

. . . .

Ankle

. . . .

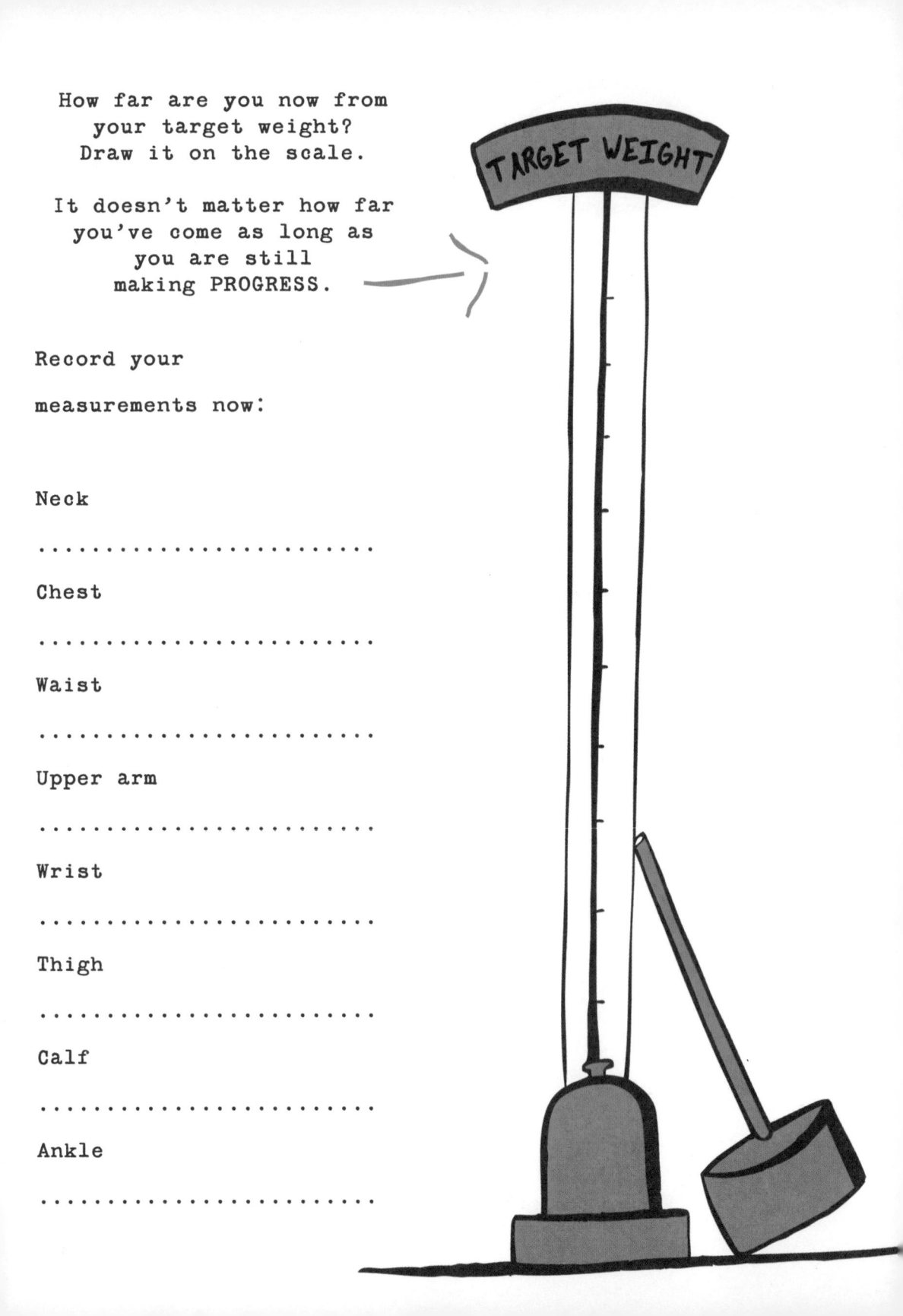

TARGET WEIGHT

THE Weigh IN

WEIGHT:
WAIST:
HEART RATE:

sunday

saturday

friday

thursday

wednesday

monday

tuesday

Log your exercise progress

week 28

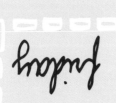

Food Diary

sunday

saturday

friday

thursday

wednesday

tuesday

monday

THE weigh-IN

WEIGHT :
WAIST :
HEART
RATE :

friday

thursday

wednesday

tuesday

monday

EXERCISE
LOG

WEEK 29

monday

tuesday

wednesday

thursday

friday

What did
you eat
today?

WEEK
30

saturday

sunday

EXERCISE LOG

WEEK 30

THE Weigh-IN

WEIGHT : _____
WAIST : _____
HEART RATE : _____

monday

tuesday

wednesday

thursday

friday

Well done!

30 weeks on your plan!

saturday

sunday

Well done!

It doesn't
end here!

Celebrate your progress and
your new way of living.

Remember you made a list of your goals?

How many have you achieved or made
progress towards reaching?

How many have you still to achieve?

What new goals can you think of?

Plan the next stage!